Bb TRUMPET

STANDARD OF EXCELL

Festival Solos

BY BRUCE PEARSON & MARY ELLEDGE

Dear Student,

Welcome to STANDARD OF EXCELLENCE FESTIVAL SOLOS, a collection of fifteen solo songs written for young musicians. For many musicians, playing solos is the greatest of all musical experiences. It allows you the opportunity to express yourself and to explore new musical challenges. FESTIVAL SOLOS includes classic solo literature written by many great composers. Playing the solos in this book will provide you with unparalleled musical experiences.

Included with your book is a professionally recorded CD of all the solos in the book. Each solo has two tracks. The first track provides a model for you, with a professional musician playing your part with piano accompaniment. The second track is the piano accompaniment only with which you can play along. You may also choose to play your solos with a live piano accompanist. The Piano Accompaniment book is available separately.

We hope you enjoy playing your solos.

Best wishes,

Bruce Pearson

Mary Elledge

TABLE OF CONTENTS

	Pages	CD Tracks		Pages	CD Tracks
INTRODUCTION		1	BAGATELLE	10	19/20
			Anton Diabelli		
TUNING NOTE		2	COUNTRY DANCE	11	21/22
MELODY	2	3/4	Ludwig van Beethoven		
Albert Biehl			SERENADE FROM "DON GIOVANNI"	12	23/24
SPRINGTIME WALTZ	3	5/6	Wolfgang Amadeus Mozart		
Franz Behr			CONCERT ETUDE	13	25/26
MARCH FROM "SCIPIO"	4	7/8	Henri Lemoine		
George Frideric Handel			ST. ANTHONY CHORALE AND RONDO	14	27/28
MENUETT	5	9/10	Franz Joseph Haydn		
Johann Philipp Kirnberger			MINUETTO	15	29/30
WOODEN SHOE DANCE	6	11/12	Ludwig van Beethoven		
Victor Herbert			COUNTRY GARDENS	16	31/32
CAVATINA	7	13/14	Traditional English Folk Song		
Wolfgang Amadeus Mozart			SCALE STUDIES	17	
CAPRICCIO	8	15/16	PROGRAM NOTES	18-20	
Daniel Turk			CONCLUSION		33
DANCE SONG	9	17/18			
Sperontes					

ISBN 0-8497-5672-3

KJOS NEIL A. KJOS MUSIC COMPANY, PUBLISHER   W28TP

Melody

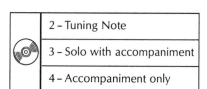

2 – Tuning Note
3 – Solo with accompaniment
4 – Accompaniment only

Albert Biehl (1836-1899)
Op. 44, No. 6

Springtime Waltz

| 2 – Tuning Note |
| 5 – Solo with accompaniment |
| 6 – Accompaniment only |

Franz Behr (1837-1898)

March from "Scipio"

| 2 – Tuning Note |
| 7 – Solo with accompaniment |
| 8 – Accompaniment only |

George Frideric Handel (1685-1759)

Maestoso (♩ = 108)

mf

mf – 1st time
p – 2nd time

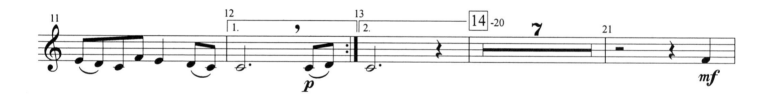

MENUETT

2 – Tuning Note	
9 – Solo with accompaniment	
10 – Accompaniment only	

Johann Philipp Kirnberger (1721-1783)

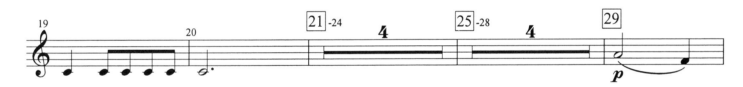

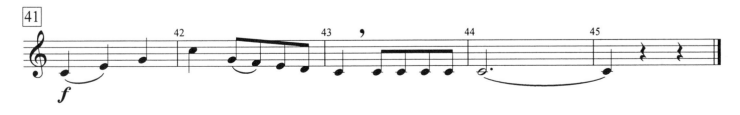

WOODEN SHOE DANCE

2 – Tuning Note	
11 – Solo with accompaniment	
12 – Accompaniment only	

Victor Herbert (1859-1924)

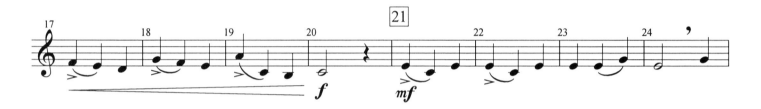

Cavatina

2 – Tuning Note	
13 – Solo with accompaniment	
14 – Accompaniment only	

Wolfgang Amadeus Mozart (1756-1791)

Capriccio

| 2 – Tuning Note |
| 15 – Solo with accompaniment |
| 16 – Accompaniment only |

Daniel Turk (1750-1813)

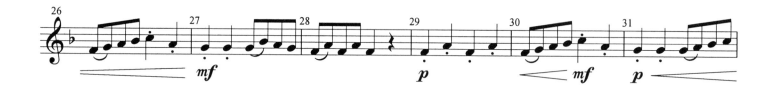

✳ DANCE SONG

2 – Tuning Note	
17 – Solo with accompaniment	
18 – Accompaniment only	

Sperontes (1705-1750)

Moderato (♩ = 112)

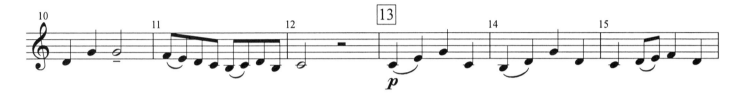

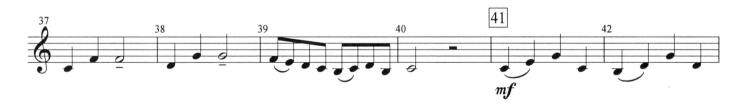

Bagatelle

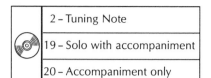

Anton Diabelli (1781-1858)
Op.125, No.10

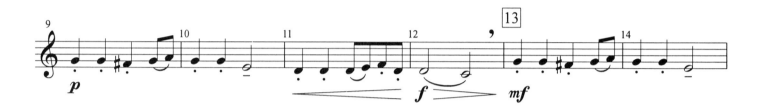

COUNTRY DANCE

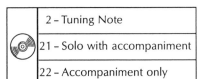

2 – Tuning Note	
21 – Solo with accompaniment	
22 – Accompaniment only	

Ludwig van Beethoven (1770-1827)

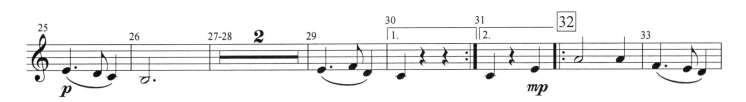

SERENADE FROM "DON GIOVANNI"

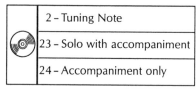

2 – Tuning Note	
23 – Solo with accompaniment	
24 – Accompaniment only	

Wolfgang Amadeus Mozart (1756-1791)

Concert Etude

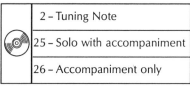

| 2 – Tuning Note |
| 25 – Solo with accompaniment |
| 26 – Accompaniment only |

Henri Lemoine (1786-1854)
Op. 37

ST. ANTHONY CHORALE AND RONDO

2 – Tuning Note	
27 – Solo with accompaniment	
28 – Accompaniment only	

Franz Joseph Haydn (1732-1809)

MINUETTO

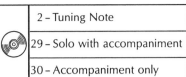

Ludwig van Beethoven (1770-1827)

Country Gardens

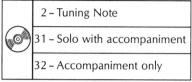

2 – Tuning Note	
31 – Solo with accompaniment	
32 – Accompaniment only	

Traditional English Folk Song

SCALE STUDIES

PROGRAM NOTES

MELODY
Albert Biehl (1836-1899)

A period of music exploration began in the days of Albert Biehl. Composers set out to expand their use of tone colors, chords and harmonies, dynamics, pitches, and tempos in their music as well as to create a greater sense of expressiveness. This time in music history is referred to as the Romantic Period (1820-1900). *Melody* represents music from the Romantic Period.

SPRINGTIME WALTZ
Franz Behr (1837-1898)

Franz Behr was born in Mecklenburg, a town in northeast Germany. Behr enjoyed writing for children and his compositions, which included popular melodies, were very tuneful. Many of his pieces were published and often written under assumed names such as "William Cooper," "Charles Morley," and "Francesco d'Orso." A waltz is a dance in triple ($\frac{3}{4}$) meter that evolved from the 18th Century.

MARCH FROM "SCIPIO"
George Frideric Handel (1685-1759)

George Frideric Handel and Johann Sebastian Bach were both born in 1685 in Germany, less than 100 miles from one another. While the two never met, they both became known as the two most influential Baroque composers. Their lives and their music differed greatly. Bach came from a musical family; Handel did not. Bach always lived near his home and his music was scholarly and religious. Handel traveled widely and was interested in all kinds of music. During his life, Handel was best known as an opera composer and wrote over 40 operas. This selection comes from his opera *Scipione*. The *March* is part of the overture preceding the first act.

MENUETT
Johann Philipp Kirnberger (1721-1783)

German composer Kirnberger was a great admirer of Johann Sebastian Bach. He studied with Bach for two years, and after, continued to study Bach's stylistic writing by searching for original manuscripts, studying them, and then producing his own compositions. Kirnberger's writings are considered remarkable for being an accurate example of the music written in the classical style. He wrote many choral and clavier (a stringed keyboard instrument) works. Menuett is the German spelling of "Minuet," a dance form in triple ($\frac{3}{4}$) meter that preceded the waltz.

WOODEN SHOE DANCE
Victor Herbert (1859-1924)

Although born in Dublin, Ireland, Herbert lived in America most of his life. While Herbert was a fine cello player, his greatest success came from writing operettas that earned him tremendous popularity. Operettas are commonly defined as light opera with dialogue. Herbert wrote more than 40 operettas and was given the title "Prince of the Operetta." *Wooden Shoe Dance* is from the operetta *Sweethearts*.

CAVATINA Wolfgang Amadeus Mozart (1756-1791)

Born in Salzburg, Austria, Mozart was a musical genius at a young age. At age three, he picked out melodies at the keyboard. At four, he began playing violin and began composing. By seven, he could play the organ with the skill of a master. He wrote his first symphony at eight and his first opera at twelve. This selection is from Mozart's opera *Don Giovanni*. It was completed in 1787, when he was 31 years old. A cavatina is a short and playful solo song.

CAPRICCIO Daniel Turk (1750-1813)

A capriccio is a vocal or instrumental piece that is lively in nature. Daniel Turk was a German violinist, organist, music theorist, and composer. He loved to perform and was held in high esteem by his peers. He composed instructional pieces, sonatas and sonatinas for piano as well as one opera, church music, symphonies, and organ pieces.

DANCE SONG Sperontes (1705-1750)

Although listed in music references under "Sperontes," his real name is Johann Sigismund Scholze. He is a German composer who loved poetry and often wrote music to fit the poetic line. One of his collections contained 250 poems with 248 musical settings. These songs were very popular in his day and are still heard and played today.

BAGATELLE Anton Diabelli (1781-1858)

Diabelli was born in Mattsee, Austria, near Salzburg. He was a music teacher, a music publisher, editor, and composer. He taught piano and guitar and in 1818, set up a music publishing firm. The firm became well known for publishing simple arrangements of popular pieces that allowed amateurs to play these songs at home. Diabelli's publishing company continued its success in more serious music circles by becoming the first to publish works by Franz Schubert. Diabelli loved writing music for children and the playfulness of his style can be heard in *Bagatelle*. A bagatelle is a short piece of music in a light style.

COUNTRY DANCE Ludwig van Beethoven (1770-1827)

Beethoven was born in Germany just 14 years after Mozart. When Beethoven was 16, Mozart heard him play and said, "Keep your eyes on him; someday he will give the world something to talk about." Beethoven moved to Vienna at the age of 22 when he became very serious about composing. He had many grand ideas about music and kept his ideas in a notebook so he could remember them. He would often refer to these ideas, rework them, and make them as perfect as possible. Beethoven wrote masterpieces in all musical forms from symphonies, piano concertos, string quartets, to piano sonatas. Along with his many large works, he wrote over 100 small pieces such as *Country Dance*.

SERENADE FROM "DON GIOVANNI"   Wolfgang Amadeus Mozart (1756-1791)

Like *Cavatina*, this selection is also from Mozart's opera *Don Giovanni*. The first performance of this opera was in 1787 in Prague, one of the most picturesque cities in Europe. Mozart himself conducted the premiere, which was a huge success. In Prague, *Don Giovanni* was greatly loved and became part of the standard opera repertory. It was performed over 500 times within the following century. The opera came to America in 1826 and continues today to be a favorite for audiences all over the world.

CONCERT ETUDE   Henri Lemoine (1786-1854)

An etude is an instructional piece of music designed to focus on a certain aspect of instrumental technique. The purpose of this etude is to concentrate on the various articulation and dynamic contrasts while striving to create an expressive, flowing melody. French composer Henri Lemoine studied at the Paris Conservatory, taught piano, wrote educational materials for piano, and later took over his father's music publishing firm.

ST. ANTHONY CHORALE AND RONDO   Franz Joseph Haydn (1732-1809)

Born in Austria, Haydn worked his way up from the most humble circumstances to one of the most celebrated composers in the world. He worked as the court composer for Prince Esterházy for over thirty years, supplying music for royal entertainment. Haydn is best known for his numerous symphonies and string quartets, but also wrote concertos, church compositions, and many pieces for voice and piano. *St. Anthony Chorale and Rondo* is part of a larger work that was written for Prince Esterházy.

MINUETTO   Ludwig van Beethoven (1770-1827)

Many composers use the title "Minuet" for their compositions. A minuet is a dance form of French origin that played an important role in instrumental music. The Minuet was a grand, dignified court dance and received its name from the small dainty step used in its performance (*menu* meaning small). Minuets are written in triple ($\frac{3}{4}$) meter and usually played at a moderate tempo. Minuetto is the Italian spelling of "Minuet."

COUNTRY GARDENS   Traditional English Folk Song

Country Gardens was written in the early 20th Century. It is said that the melody is derived from a medieval source. The source was collected by a musicologist, Cecil Sharp, who hiked all over the British Isles gathering melodies and songs from natives. The tune, later arranged for piano, was published and became extremely popular. Sources say that, originally, this tune was called *Handkerchief Dance*.